A World of Tea Parties
Just For Kids

Written by Pat Nekola

Illustrated by C. DeWitt

ISBN: 978-0-9796523-6-3 ⟶

Library of Congress Cataloging Number: 2012935536

Published by:
Applewood Ink
A division of Catering by Design
P.O. Box 181
Waukesha, WI 53187

Dedication

I would like to dedicate this book to all the children ages 5-10 having fun while learning about tea parties and practicing good manners, especially using "please" and "thank you" throughout their daily lives. Miss Lacey says those words are music to her ears.

Washington Tea Elementary
101 Tea Cup Lane

Grades Kindergarten through 5th Grade

At the end of each school year Miss Lacey, the school librarian, helps the fifth graders from her World Tea Party Club give a tea party for the first and second grade students. She got the idea to have a world tea party while traveling to different countries on her summer vacations. She attended teas in every country and found them very fascinating and fun.

Miss Lacey

Miss Lacey is a tall striking blonde with big blue eyes and apple plum checks. She loves the students and interacts with each student very well. She formed a World Tea Club and expressed that all students are welcome. She is an excellent cook and very well versed on how to organize a tea party. Several students attended her club after school to learn about theme tea parties and the basic social skills such as please and thank you. They especially enjoyed her ideas about theme tea parties just for kids.

Miss Lacey's Teapot and Teacup Sets

Each year she visited a different country and purchased a teapot with matching tea cups and plates. At the end of the year she displayed the individual sets in her display case outside the library door hallway. She received many questions and comments.

In the showcase there were tea sets on the top shelf from Japan, a Russian Samovar with gilded glass and a tea set from China. The bottom shelf displayed a children's tea set, a red and white checked set from America and a Victorian set from England.

Display of Flag and Tea Party Books for the Different Countries.

She had another showcase inside the library to display flags and tea party books from different countries.

How To Hold The Tea Cup

Miss Lacey had each student practice how to hold a tea cup. The thumb and the forefinger holds the handle of the cup while the little pinkie finger flairs out a little.

How To Hold The Tea Cup

Miss Lacey welcomed every student to her World Tea Club and said, "I have brought a collection of tea cups today. We are going to practice how to hold a tea cup. To practice how to hold a tea cup, the thumb and forefinger hold the handle of the cup while the little pinkie finger flairs out a little."

Next, she asked why they decided to join her club. Most students said that it would be fun to give and attend a tea. Miss Lacey explained that tea parties are not new, but have always been part of the culture of various countries. In recent years theme teas have become very popular, especially in the United States. Often children attend etiquette tea parties or have tea parties for their birthdays. It is fun to dress up for any theme tea party, eat the finger foods, drink tea, play games or just socialize with others in the group.

An Example of How to Write an Invitation

The outside of the invitation can say, "You are invited to a Busy Bee Tea Party!".

Use the following words as a guide on the invitation

Please join us in honor of Grace
Date: January 27 and year
Time: 2-4 p.m.
Location: Address, City, State and Zip
R.S.V.P

Outside can say:
You are invited to a
Busy Bee Tea Party!
In honor of Grace
given by Mrs. Go
at 2626 Apple Tree Lane
City, State and Zip
Sunday, January 27 and Year
2-4 p.m.
R.S.V.P. by January 17 and Year

You are invited to a
Busy Bee Tea Party!

In honor of Grace,
given by Mrs. Go

Please join us in honor of Grace
Date: Sunday, January 27, (year)
Time: 2-4 p.m.
Location: 2626 Apple Tree Lane,
City, State and Zip
Please RSVP by January 17th

Note: R.S.V.P. is French (résponzes s'il vois plaît). This phrase literally translates as "respond if you please or simply please respond." Miss Lacey said it is only polite to respond either through mail or a telephone call. If it is a surprise, be sure you let the hostess quietly know so you will not spoil the surprise. The hostess needs to know how many guests are coming so she can plan on food, seating arrangements, party favors, and entertainment.

illustration by Galaxy Ynocencio

RUSSIAN:
Puzhalsta (puh-jah-stah)
Spasibi (spah-ssee-boh)

ENGLAND:
Please
Thank You

JAPANESE:
Kudasi (koodahsi)
Arigatou (ahree-gah-tow)

FRENCH:
S'il vous plâit (see voo play)
Merci (mehr-see)

USA:
Please
Thank You

CHINESE/ MANDARIN:
Qing (cheeng)
Xiexie (syeh-syeh)

Miss Lacey Practices with the Children How to Say Please and Thank You in the Different Languages.

Please and Thank you in other languages:

England: **Please**
              Thank You

Russian: **Please-Puzhalsta** (puh-jah-stah)
              Thank You-Spasibi (spah-see-boh)

Japenesse: **Please-Kudasi** (koodahsi)
              Thank You-Arigato (ahree-gah-tow)

Chinese/Mandarin: **Please-Qing** (cheeng)
              Thank You-Xie-Xie (syeh-syeh)

French: **Please-S'il Vois Plâit** (see voo play)
              Thank You-Merci (mehr-see)

American: **Please**
              Thank You

Miss Lacey stressed the importance of please and thank you in every country. It is only courteous to thank the hostess for giving the tea party. Always compliment the hostess for having such a lovely party. When attending a tea as a guest, it is important to say, "Will you please pass the tea cookies?" Once the tea cookies are passed to you, say, "Thank You." The guest then passes the cookies and says, "You are welcome." She explained, that in China, these are the three words that are expected from every person in their country including visitors. She also added that please, thank you and you are welcome are appreciated in all countries.

Miss Lacey said that a hand written thank you note is a must after attending any party or if you received a gift at the party. It is just polite and proper to let the hostess know you appreciated the invitation and for having a nice party. Be sure the thank you note is sent to the hostess no later than one month after the party.

Thank You Notes
to Miss Lacey

Thank You

Dear Miss Lacey,

Thank you for hosting the tea party. It was very fun to play the games and eat the food.

Sincerely,
Mickey

Thank You

Dear Miss Lacey and 5th grade class,

Thank you for hosting the poodle party. It was very fun and a big surprise. I hope to be part of the tea club again next year. I learned a lot about teas.

Sincerely,
Jena

Katie Talks About the Tea Setup and What They Liked About the Tea

Miss Lacey asked the students to tell her if any of them had ever attended a tea party. Katie, age 10, raised her hand and told the club that she and her sister, Ana, had been to an "Ant Tea for My Sister and Me." Katie's grandmother had promised her granddaughters a summer picnic tea, but had gotten sick and was unable to have the tea party. Her friend, Mrs. Cola, said that she would have a surprise menu and that the girls would dress up for the party. When Katie and her sister arrived for the party, they each picked out a hat to wear and put on a shawl made of red and white checked material with black ants.

Miss Lacey asked, "Katie, what is a menu?"

"Well, I know it has food," Katie replied.

"Correct," said Miss Lacey. " A menu is a list of foods served at a meal. What were some of the items served at your special tea?"

"Mrs. Cola called them finger foods and gave Ana and me the recipes," Katie said.

"What is a recipe?" asked Miss Lacey.

Katie answered, "It is any food that can be eaten with your fingers such as a small sandwich or teacake. Ana and I do not like tea so Mrs. Cola served us our favorite lemonade. I am interested in learning about tea and I want to like tea. My dad took pictures of our tea party. I brought them and the recipes to share with the club."

Miss Lacey asked Katie to tell the club where the tea party took place and expound on the decorations.

Katie explained that the party was held outside in Mrs. Cola's garden at a round table. The table was covered with a tablecloth of the red and white checked material with the printed black ants. There was a flower centerpiece with ribbons of the same material.

"Everything matched," explained Katie. "Ana and I had so much fun dressing up and we liked the food very much."

"Did you do an activity?" asked Miss Lacey.

"We just told Mrs. Cola about our exciting trip to San Francisco," answered Katie.

Miss Lacey then thanked Katie for bringing the pictures and recipes and telling the club about the very special tea party.

.

The Ant Tea Party for
My Sister and Me

The Ant Tea Party for My Sister and Me Menu

Teapot Finger Sandwiches

Mini Hot Dogs on Crescent Rolls

Finger Fruits

Petite Brownies Frosted
with
Chocolate Caramel Butter Cream Frosting

Pink Lemonade

Teapot Finger Sandwiches

Yield: 16 sandwiches

1-pound 8 ounce loaf whole wheat bread
1-pound 8 ounce loaf white bread
1-10 ounce package sliced ham
1-10 ounce package shredded carrots
1 stick butter or margarine
1 small size teapot cookie cutter
1-4 inch doily

Using a teapot cookie cutter, cut out one teapot from each top slice of bread. Using an aspic star cookie cutter, cut out the center of the top slice of bread. Match up the bottom and top of each teapot. Butter the bottom and top of each teapot. Cut out 3 teapots from each slice of ham. Place one teapot ham slice on the bottom of the each teapot shaped bread. Place the top teapot piece over each ham teapot to make the tea sandwich. Cut one shredded carrot in half. Make a cross with the carrot and place it into the center of the cut out star to form an x. Arrange the finger sandwiches on a platter lined with a doily.

Mini Hot Dogs on Crescent Rolls

Yield: 40 pieces

1 pound hot dogs
1-8 ounce can crescent rolls

Dry off the hot dogs with a paper towel. Roll one crescent roll around each hot dog. Bake at 375F on an ungreased pan for 12 to 15 minutes or until golden brown. Cut each crescent roll with hot dog into 5 pieces. Serve hot.

Finger Fruits

Yield: 6 servings

1 pound green grapes
1 orange sliced
6 strawberries
frilled tooth picks

continued on next page

Place 3 grapes per frilled toothpick. Slice 5 orange slices from the orange. Cut each orange slice halfway down. Overlap each orange slice and place one toothpick through the center of each strawberry. Place strawberry into the center of the slightly overlapped orange. Place grapes on the outside of each side of the serving plate. Place the strawberry orange fruit in the center of the plate. Serve cold.

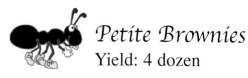 ## Petite Brownies
Yield: 4 dozen

1-19.5 ounce box dark chocolate brownie mix
$\frac{1}{2}$ cup oil
$\frac{1}{4}$ cup water
2 eggs
1 Bundt tea cake and candy mold pan with 30 cavities
baking spray

Add the oil, water and eggs to the brownie mix. Stir until mixed together. Spray each cavity with baking spray. Fill each cavity about $\frac{2}{3}$ full. Bake at 350F for about 15 minutes. Remove from oven and cool for about 2-3 minutes on a cooling rack. Gently remove each petite brownie; continue to cool brownies. Wash out the Bundt pan. Dry thoroughly. Spray 18 cavities with baking spray. Repeat filling cavities. Bake the second pan at 350F for about 15 minutes and follow the same directions as for the first 30 baked petite brownie cakes.

 ## Chocolate Caramel Butter Cream Frosting
Yield: 48 frosted Petite Brownie Cakes

1 stick butter, softened
2 cups powdered sugar
2 tablespoon water
$\frac{1}{2}$ teaspoon caramel flavoring
$\frac{1}{2}$ teaspoon imitation chocolate flavoring
$\frac{1}{4}$ teaspoon salt
1-1 C cake tube
144 raisins (for entire batch or
 18 for 6 brownies)
1-4 inch doily

continued on next page

18

Beat together butter, powedered sugar, water, caramel and chocolate flavorings and salt. Place frosting in a pastry bag with a number 1 C cake tube. Place one frosting star on top of each brownie. Top each frosting star with 3 raisins forming a circle to look like ants on each frosting star. Serve brownies on a footed glass plate lined with a doily.

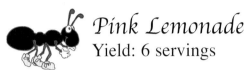 *Pink Lemonade*
Yield: 6 servings

1-12 fluid ounces pink lemonade
4 cans cold water
1 large lemon, sliced

Place lemonade in a pitcher. Add the water and stir thoroughly. Transfer into a red teapot adorned with a sleeve with red and white check ant pattern. Place a slit halfway up the lemon and attach it to the top of the glass. Serve in glasses with matching sleeves to the teapot.

The History
of Tea in Russia

Tea in Russia

The majority of Russians drink tea daily. Russians drink tea from a glass inside a gilded holder. Please look at the picture of a tea party taken place in Mytishchi Vasily Perov in 1862. (See page 20) Tea drinking is a family affair and it is taken very seriously in Russia.

What is a samovar?

A samovar is literally a "self-boiler." It is a heated container to heat and boil water and used in Russia to keep the tea hot all day long. The samovar used coal, pine cones or charcoal in the traditional times but now can be purchased electric to boil the water. A traditional style samovar has a large metal container with a faucet almost to the bottom and a metal pipe that runs vertically through the middle. Most samovars are made out of brass, bronze, copper, silver, gold, tin or nickel. The fuel inside the samovar heats the water in the surrounding container. After the fire is off, a teapot can be placed on top to help keep the water hot due to passing hot air. Russians often drink a strong tea called zavarka. If the fire is going faint it can be rekindled with the help of bellows. Most people associate the Russians with the samovar even though other countries also use them. Check out the illustration of the samovar and the glass of tea inside the gilded glass holder used by the Russians to better understand how the Russians made and drank tea. (See page 27)

Tea was introduced to Russia in 1638 when the Mongolian ruler gave Czar Michael 250 pounds of tea as a gift. At first the Czar refused the tea, but, with some friendly persuasion, the Czar accepted the tea. By 1669 China was exporting tea supplies with a camel caravan and the Russians exchanged furs in return. China continued to send tea to Russia. Catherine the Great made it possible to export tea to Russia from 1736-1796 (the year of her death). When Russia purchased 3 million pounds of loose tea and tea bricks, the price was lower and even the middle class could afford to drink tea.

Do you know how tea was imported?
a. Train
b. Airplane
c. Camel caravan

The answer is c.

A trip with the camel caravan known as a Russian Caravan could take as long as 16-18 months. The smokey flavor of tea was due to the caravan's campfires.

Not until 1880 did the faster train service deliver the tea and take the place of camel caravans. By the mid 19th century China declined in sending tea to Russia. Russia began to buy tea from London and also Odessa, a province in Ukraine. It is located on the northwest shore of the Black Sea and is the fourth largest city in Ukraine. Also note that the horse drawn tea transport ended in 1905.

Black tea is generally served in Russia and the Imperial family drank caravan tea which is a blend of India and China black teas. Sugar and milk is also served with this style of tea. The Russians also used jams or honey in their tea. They sometimes used lemons studded with cloves. Some Russians drank tea with a sugar cube between their teeth. Green tea also became popular in Russia.

Club, you now have a little history about tea in Russia. Let's make some blini, Russian tea cakes and Russian black tea.

The Blin or Blintz

As Miss Lacey researched the blin or blintz, she learned that blintzes come from the Yiddish (Jewish) fare. The Russians call them blin (plural is blini), so she will refer to the term as "blini". This is a Russian version not unlike a crépe. Traditionally, Russians made the blini with a ratio of buckwheat flour to regular flour and was a yeasted batter. The blini were often made in the Spring, resembling little suns and signifying the end of winter. The tradition was that everyone took a turn stirring the batter and thus symbolizing "sharing of work." The tradition must have come right out of the Communist Revolution. Actually the blini are flat thin pancakes. The Russians filled them with smoked salmon and sour cream or caviar. However, for the first grade tea, we will use the recipe below.

Peanut Butter and Jelly Blini
Yield: 40 Blini

1$\frac{1}{4}$ cups flour
$\frac{1}{2}$ teaspoon salt
$\frac{3}{4}$ teaspoon baking powder
2 eggs, beaten
1$\frac{1}{2}$ cups half and half or evaporated milk
$\frac{1}{2}$ cup water
1 teaspoon vanilla
2 tablespoons sugar
2 tablespoons butter, melted and cooled

Filling
1 pound 3 ounce jar creamy peanut butter
1-12 ounce jar of strawberry preserves

Garnish
1-12 ounce container non-dairy frozen whipped topping, thawed
12 fresh strawberries, hulled and sliced
plus 22 whole strawberries with hulls

Combine flour, salt and baking powder in a bowl. Set aside. In a large bowl combine the beaten eggs, the half and half, water, vanilla and sugar. Add the flour mixture and stir until very smooth with no lumps. Stir in the melted butter. Heat two mini 4 inch fry pans and spray with non-stick cooking spray. Swirl 1

continued on next page

tablespoon of the batter into each pan and cook until edges are dry, (about 1 minute). With a spatula, flip the blin over and cook briefly on the other side. As each blin finishes cooking, stack on top of each other with a waxed paper or parchment paper square in between.

To Fill and Serve:
Spread each blin with 2 teaspoons peanut butter and 1 teaspoon preserves. Fold each of two sides into the center of the circle, making a long strip. Fold each end of the strip into the center making a square. Place blini on a footed tray, seam side down, and garnish each with a dollop of whipped topping and a strawberry slice. Place whole strawberries on the footed platter around the edge of the 9 inch glass plate. Serve at your Russian theme tea.

Russian Tea Cakes
Yield: 3 dozen

1 cup butter
1 cup powdered sugar, divided
1 teaspoon vanilla
2$\frac{1}{4}$ cups flour
$\frac{1}{4}$ teaspoon salt
$\frac{3}{4}$ cup finely chopped walnuts

Mix together butter and $\frac{1}{2}$ cup powdered sugar and add vanilla. Add the flour, salt, and walnuts. Stir until all the ingredients hold together well. Roll into 1 inch balls. Place on an ungreased baking sheet. Bake at 400F for 10-15 minutes. While still warm, roll in powdered sugar. Cool on cooling racks.

How to Make Russian Tea
Yield: 6 servings

1$\frac{1}{2}$ cups water
$\frac{1}{2}$ cup sugar
1 cup orange juice
1 cup pineapple juice
Juice from 1 lemon

In a tea ball or cheesecloth add
2-2 inch cinnamon sticks

continued on next page

6 cloves
6 allspice
4 teaspoons tea leaves or 2 tea bags
Combine sugar, water, orange and pineapple juice. Also add juice from 1 lemon. Add the tea ball or cheesecloth with spices. Bring to a boil; remove from the heat. Add the tea and steep for 3 minutes. Remove tea. Leave spices in until it suits your taste. Keep on low heat until ready to serve.

What does steep mean?
1. Boil water with tea bags
2. Simmer water for 30 minutes
3. Remove from heat and soak tea bag thoroughly in hot water.

The answer is 3.

Black plate with painted flowers, used at tea time in some families in Russia.

Matryoshka Doll

The Matryoshka doll is a Russian nesting doll and is considered as a toy. It is a set of wooden dolls of decreasing size placed one inside the other. The first set was carved in 1890. It takes a lot of skill to carve these dolls. Folk painters painted the dolls.

A Russian Doll Craft
for Seating Arrangement of Guests
Yield: 1 Matryoshka bottle

1 chili sauce bottle
green crepe paper
hot pink crepe paper
clear tape ³/₄ inch wide
7 pictures of a Matryoshka doll, cut out
1 stem of leaves
1 tea bag wrapper with tea leaf picture
3 tea bags
1 name tag
1 glue stick
1-4 inch round glass plate.

Cut two pieces of green crepe paper 8 inches long and one piece 11 inches long and ³/₄ inches wide. Cut one piece of hot pink crepe paper 8 inches long and one piece 12 inches long and ³/₄ inches wide. Starting at the bottom of the chili sauce bottle, alternately wrap the green and hot pink crepe paper around the bottle overlapping the colors. Place tape at the top of the of crepe paper to hold together. At the top of the bottle wrap the 11 inch x ³/₄ inch wide piece of green crepe paper and tie the two ends together with the ends extending. Place one stem of leaves into the bottle. Glue one doll picture onto the center back of the bottle. At random, glue the remaining doll pictures onto the front of the bottle and also leaves. Type up each guest's name. Cut out the guest's name and glue onto the front top of each chili bottle. Place the bottle onto the 4 inch round plate. Place one doll craft at each guest's place setting. Also use this doll craft as a gift for each guest.

Russian Samovar and Gilded Glasses.

Miss Lacey told the club that their next tea theme is very neat. It is a "**Busy Bee Tea**." Here are some tips to better help you understand how to decorate for a tea and also the order of a menu. The picture shows the guest table setup.

Busy Bee Tea Menu

Chicken Nuggets

Biscuits, Beehive Butter and Honey

Mini Blueberry Muffins

Beehive Cheese Spread

Mini Bread Sticks

Apples with Fruit Kabobs

Mini Peanut Butter Kisses

Mini Peanut Butter and Jelly Cookies

Mini Decorated Sugar Cookies

Apple Juice

Chicken Nuggets
Yield: 6

Purchase the amount needed for the tea at your favorite fast food restaurant or from the local grocery store in the frozen food department. For heating the frozen chicken nuggets follow the package directions.

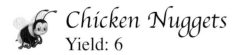 ## Busy Bee Biscuits
Yield:6

6 pre-baked biscuits
6 petal baking cup liners
6 bee shaped picks

Place one biscuit into each baking cup liner. Place one bee shaped pick into the center of each biscuit. Serve on a round 10 inch platter.

 ## Butter
Yield: 6

$\frac{1}{2}$ cup butter, softened
1 beehive pick

Beat the butter. Place butter into a cake decorating bag with a number 19 cake tube, form butter into a beehive. Place one bee pick into the middle of the butter spread and the other one into the mini bread sticks.

 ## Honey
Yield: 6

1-16 ounce jar honey
6 small serving bowls
6 honey dippers

Fill the bowls a little less than half full. Place one honey dipper into each bowl. Serve with the biscuits.

Mini Blueberry Muffins
Yield: 24 mini muffins

2 cups flour
4 teaspoons baking powder
$^1/_2$ teaspoon salt
$^1/_4$ cup sugar
1 egg, beaten
$^1/_4$ cup butter, melted
1 cup milk
1 cup blueberries
1 mini muffin pan
24 mini muffin liners
1 doily
4 foiled wrapped chocolate bees
3 foiled wrapped chocolate flowers

Mix together flour, baking powder, salt and sugar. Stir the blueberries into the dry ingredients. Mix together egg, butter and milk. Fold the wet ingredients into the dry ingredients just enough to moisten the batter. Using a mini portion control scoop, fill muffin liners about $^2/_3$ full. Bake at 400F for 10-12 minutes or until toothpick inserted in the center of the muffin comes out clean. Remove muffins from the pan. Cool thoroughly. Gently remove the liners from the muffins. Place 9 muffins on a small tray lined with a doily. Garnish with foiled wrapped chocolate bees and flowers.

Beehive Cheese Spread with Mini Bread Sticks
Yield: 6-10 servings

6 ounces of cheddar cheese spread, softened
4 ounces cream cheese, softened
$^1/_2$ teaspoon Worcestershire sauce
1 beehive pick
1-5 ounce package mini bread sticks

Beat together the cheddar cheese spread and cream cheese. Add the Worcestershire sauce and continue to beat until smooth and creamy. In a small round serving bowl and using a number 32 cake tube, form cheese into a beehive. Place one bee shaped pick into the middle of the cheese spread and one into the middle of the bread sticks. Serve with the mini bread sticks.

Apples with Fruit Kabobs
Yield: 8-10 servings

3 honey crisp or gala apples
1 pound grapes, cleaned
$\frac{1}{2}$ pint raspberries, cleaned
1-8 ounce can pineapple chunks, drained
10 decorative picks

Remove the stem from one apple and place the stem side down on the middle of the plate. Cut two apples in half. Place the 4 halves of apples on the plate with clumps of grapes in between each apple half. Fill each kabob with 2 raspberries and one pineapple chunk, starting and ending with the raspberries and the pineapple chunk in the middle. Insert kabobs into the center apple and the center of each outside apple.

Mini Peanut Butter Kisses
Yield: 1 dozen

1-17.5 ounce package peanut butter cookie mix
1 tablespoon water
3 tablespoons vegetable oil
1 egg
12 chocolate kisses
1 doily

Preheat oven to 375F. Mix the water, oil and egg with the cookie mix. Divide dough in half and set one half aside to make the peanut butter and jelly cookies. Using a mini portion control scoop, form each cookie into a ball. Flatten each cookie with the heel of your hand. Place a small thumb print in the middle of each cookie. Bake on an ungreased baking sheet for 7-10 minutes or until golden brown. Remove pan from the oven and cool slightly. Place one chocolate candy kiss in the center of each cookie. Remove cookies from the baking sheet and place on a cooling rack. Arrange on a small glass serving tray lined with a doily.

Mini Peanut Butter and Jelly Cookies
Yield: 1 dozen

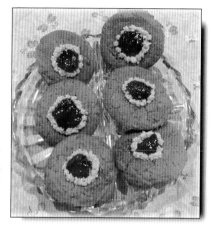

½ of peanut butter cookie dough
1-12 ounce jar strawberry preserves
1-16 ounce container white frosting
4 drops pink food coloring
1 doily

Refer to the mini peanut butter kisses for mixing the mini peanut butter and jelly cookies. The dough is divided between the mini peanut butter kisses and mini peanut butter and jelly cookies. Using a mini portion control scoop, form each cookie into a ball. Flatten each cookie with the heel of your hand. Place a small thumb print in the middle of each cookie. Bake on an ungreased baking sheet for 7-10 minutes or until golden brown. Remove from the pan and place on a cooling rack. Place a small dab of strawberry preserves in the center of the thumb print of each cookie. Mix pink food coloring into the white frosting to make the pink frosting. Using a cake decorating bag and a number 13 star tip, pipe on a circle of frosting around the strawberry preserves. Place cookies on a small round serving tray lined with a doily.

Mini Decorated Sugar Cookies
Yield: 1 dozen

1 dozen packaged sugar cookies
pink frosting
12 green M&M's®
1 rectangular doily

Use the remaining pink frosting from the mini peanut butter and jelly cookies. Using a pastry bag and a number 32 cake tube, pipe on frosting in a beehive fashion. Place one M&M® standing up on its side in the middle of each cookie. Place on a small oblong glass tray lined with a doily.

Apple Juice
Yield: 1 quart

Serve apple juice at the Busy Bee Tea.

How to Make the Flowerpot Lollipop Sucker Tea Gift
Yield: 1 flowerpot sucker

1-4 inch flowerpot
1-4 inch flowerpot dish
1 small size styrofoam ball, cut in half
 (to fit the pot)
1 pink lollipop sucker
2-6 inch green fiesta picks
2 wooden bumble bees
4 broad green silk leaves
hot glue

Hot glue the bottom of the flowerpot onto the flowerpot dish. Cut styrofoam ball in half and place round part of the half ball into the pot. Place lollipop into the center of the styrofoam to secure the sucker. Place one fiesta pick into the styrofoam on each side of the lollipop. Hot glue one broad leaf on each side of the bee. Hot glue one bee on the bottom front and back of the flowerpot.

 ## How to Make a Lollipop Sucker Busy Bee Centerpiece
Yield: 1 centerpiece

1 teapot
1 styrofoam ball (cut in half)
2 wooden bees
1 (14-15) inch long, 1 inch wide lace
5 oval pink lollipops
12 wrapped pink and yellow lollipops
4 foiled wrapped flower candies
5 bee picks
25-4 inch wooden ice cream craft sticks
3 thin green leaves
5 yellow flower clumps
hot glue

Cut styrofoam ball in half. Place styrofoam ball into the flowerpot with rounded side in the teapot with flat side up. Leave $^1/_2$-$^3/_4$ inch of styrofoam sticking out of the flowerpot. Hot glue the lace to the styrofoam with lace touching the top of the teapot. Center and hot glue one wooden bee to the top of the teapot both front and back. Hot glue the 5 pink oval suckers, 8 wrapped suckers, 4 foiled wrapped flower candies, 5 bee picks, 3 leaves and the 5 flower clumps to the craft sticks. Arrange the candies in the teapot.

How to Make the Busy Bee Tea Scarf
Yield: 1

1 strip bee material 8-9 inches wide and 42 inches long
pink thread or pinking shears
hot glue
1 wooden busy bee
1 steel pin back (1 inch brass)

Serge the edges of the scarf with pink thread to form the rolled hem or turn hem over $\frac{1}{4}$ inch twice on all 4 sides and stitch to form a narrow hem, or pink the edges. Hot glue the steel pin back onto the back of the bee. On the day of the tea, place the scarf around the child's neck and crisscross; place one bee pin through the two thicknesses of the scarf to secure the scarf in place. (See the Busy Bee Tea Scarf on page 9).

How to Make the Busy Bee Tea Hat
Yield: 1 decorated hat

1 straw hat
1 band material 44 inches long and 4 inches wide
pink thread or pinking shears
1 wooden flower
1 bee pick
2 thin green leaves

Cut the band and serge or pink the raw edges of the band. Starting at the front of the crown of the hat, center band and tie a bow in the back of the hat. Hot glue the bee and leaves onto the flower and hot glue the flower onto the band.

How to Make the Busy Bee Table Runner
Yield: 1 table Runner

Busy bee material
pink thread or pinking shears

Measure the length of the table and add 12 inches. Cut fabric to appropriate size. Serge the edges of the material or make a rolled hem. Turn edges over $\frac{1}{4}$ inch twice on each side and stitch to form a narrow hem or pink the edges. (See runner on page 28).

When Miss Lacey finished with the "Busy Bee Tea," she reminded the club that in two weeks they would be doing **"A Holiday Tea for the Queen and King of Hearts and the Royal Family."** The names of 6 World Tea Party Club members would be drawn to participate in this holiday tea.

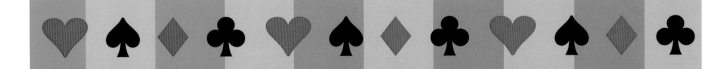

A Holiday Tea for the Queen and King of Hearts and the Royal Family Menu

Grilled Cheese Finger Sandwiches with Hearts

Teapot and Heart Shaped Cinnamon Scones

Mini Chocolate Tarts

Holiday Shortbread Cookies

Gingerbread Cookies

The Queen and King Castle Cake

Wassail

Hot Chocolate

♥ Grilled Cheese Finger Sandwiches with Hearts

Yield :9 servings

1-20 ounce loaf white bread
1 playing card
¹/₂ cup butter, softened
1-16 ounce package cheese slices
 (individually wrapped)
1 aspic heart shaped cookie cutter
1 red heart shaped doily

Place two slices bread together. Place 1 playing card sideways on the bread.
Cut out the shape of the card with a sharp knife and remove the crust. Unwrap each cheese slice and place one slice of cheese on each bottom slice of bread. Top with the second slice of bread. Butter each outside of each sandwich. Set the griddle for 375F. Place cheese sandwiches on griddle and toast each side of the sandwich until golden brown. Using an aspic heart cookie cutter, cut out a heart in the center of each card shaped grilled cheese. Line a serving tray with a red heart shaped doily. Arrange grilled cheese sandwiches on the tray. Pass the tray of sandwiches to the tea party guests.

Miss Lacey reminded the students that the guests should always be served first.

♠ Heart and Teapot Shaped Cinnamon Scones
Yield: 14 scones

¹/₂ cup cold butter
2 cups all-purpose flour
¹/₄ cup brown sugar
¹/₄ cup granulated sugar
1 tablespoon sugar
1 tablespoon baking powder
¹/₄ teaspoon salt
1 teaspoon orange flavoring
1 teaspoon cinnamon
³/₄ cup cream
1 egg

Preheat oven to 375F. Cut butter into a mixture of flour, sugars, baking powder and salt. In a separate bowl, beat together cream and egg. Slowly pour into dry ingredients, stirring with rubber spatula until dough forms. Add the orange flavoring and cinnamon and stir. Roll out dough on floured board. Cut out 7 teapot shaped and 7 heart shaped scones. Bake on ungreased cookie sheet about 20 minutes. Cool. Frost with orange glaze.

◆ Orange Glaze
Yield: 14 scones

2 cups powdered sugar
2 tablespoons butter, softened
3 tablespoons water
1 teaspoon orange flavoring
1 teaspoon orange peel
1 package crown metallic picks (12 count)
1 heart shaped doily

Add butter to powdered sugar and beat. Add the water, orange flavoring and orange peel. Beat until smooth. Frost and garnish each scone with a crown metallic pick. Place scones on a platter lined with a heart shaped doily.

♣ Mini Chocolate Tarts
Yield: 15 tarts

1-2.1 ounce box fully baked filo shells, thawed
1-6 ounce package instant chocolate pudding
1-12 ounce container non-dairy whipped topping, thawed
1-$\frac{1}{2}$ pint raspberries
1 red heart shaped doily

Prepare the pudding following the package directions. Fill each shell with a teaspoon of chocolate pudding. Using a number 849 star cake decorating tip, fill a cake bag with the non-dairy whipped topping. Pipe a star on each tart and top with one raspberry with bottom side up. Arrange the tarts on a tray lined with a heart shaped doily.

♥ Holiday Shortbread Cookies
Yield: 1-12 ounce package

1-12 ounce package holiday shortbread cookies
1 heart shaped doily

Arrange cookies on a serving tray lined with a heart shaped doily.

Mini Iced Gingerbread Cookies
Yield: 1-12 ounce package

1-12 ounce package iced gingerbread cookies
1 heart shaped doily

Arrange cookies on a serving tray lined with a heart shaped doily.

The Queen and King's Castle Cake
Yield: 1 9-inch cake (serves 10)

1-18.25 ounce yellow cake mix
eggs
water
oil
8 crown metallic picks
4 short ice cream cones
4 pointed ice cream cones
1-8 ounce package sour cherry balls
1-6 ounce package black licorice
1-5 ounce box red licorice bites
red and green M&M's®
2 graham crackers
1 chocolate candy bar
4 pounds butter cream (readymade frosting), divided
blue food coloring
1 wooden castle
1 large cake board
1-6.6 ounce package colored gold fish crackers

Follow the directions on the cake mix. Divide the batter into two 9 inch square greased cake pans. Bake at 350F for 25-30 minutes or until toothpick inserted into center of the cake comes out clean. Cool cake and frost them to form one cake. Make four turrets, one for each corner of the cake. Use one short ice cream cone for the bottom and one pointed ice cream cone for the top. Frost the two cones together to form each turret. Break off the picks on each crown and place a dab of frosting on the back of each crown. Place the crowns

continued on next page

at the top point of each ice cream cone and also at the bottom center, both front and back. Alternate red licorice pieces with chocolate squares around the top layer of the frosted cake. Decorate the roof top of the cake with the M&M's® alternating the red and green M&M's®. Color 2 cups of frosting with blue food coloring to make the water around the moat. Place the wooden castle in the center front of the cake. Spread the colored frosting around the base of the castle. Place 2 graham crackers in the front of the cake to represent the gate/bridge over the moat and use black licorice for the ropes on the side of the bridge. Place 3 sour cherry balls along the bottom of the cake on each side of the draw bridge. At random, stand up the gold fish crackers on the blue frosting around the castle.

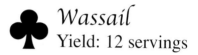

Wassail
Yield: 12 servings

2 quarts apple cider
4 oranges
2 lemons
12 whole cloves
4 cinnamon sticks
$\frac{1}{8}$ teaspoon ground ginger
$\frac{1}{8}$ teaspoon ground nutmeg
2 tablespoons sugar

Combine apple cider and juice from the oranges and lemons. Add the cloves, cinnamon sticks, ground ginger, nutmeg and sugar. Stir together. Place the mixed ingredients in the crock pot on slow heat and simmer all day and enjoy the aroma at the tea. Serve hot.

Hot Chocolate
Yield: 8 servings

$\frac{1}{3}$ cup water
$5\frac{1}{3}$ cup milk
2 cups fat-free half and half
$\frac{1}{2}$ cup cocoa
$\frac{1}{3}$ cup sugar
2 teaspoons vanilla
$1\frac{1}{2}$ cups marshmallows
1 cup chocolate chips

continued on next page

Hot Chocolate continued

1-6.5 ounce can dairy whipped topping

Mix water, milk and half and half in a pan. Add the cocoa, sugar and stir constantly over medium heat until heated through. Stir in the vanilla. Remove from the heat and and whisk until frothy. Serve with marshmallows, chocolate chips and dairy whipped topping.

♠ *How to Make a Candy Cane Heart*
Yield: 1 candy cane heart

2-6.7 ounce candy canes

Form the candy cane heart by placing each hook of the candy cane together and the end of each candy cane touching.

◆ *How to Make the Candy Heart Gift Box*
Yield: 1 gift box

1-3x3 gift treat box
4 decorative stars on picks
1 wooden heart
1 wooden crown
1 candy cane circle
1 miniature bow
$1/_3$ pound foiled wrapped heart shaped candies
hot glue

Hot glue the crown onto the front and heart onto the back of the box. Place the candy cane circle upright and glue to the inside bottom of the box. Hot glue the star in the middle. Hot glue the miniature bow onto the center of the candy cane circle. Place stars into the center of the basket at different heights. Fill with candy shaped hearts.

♣ *How to Make the Guest Place Card*
Yield: 1 guest place card

1 package of place cards (3x4 inches)
1 package name tags with playing card design
  (2x4 inches) with adhesive
1 package of paper with card symbols
names of the children
pinking sears
1 glue stick

Glue the card design on the lower back of the place card. Adhere the name tag to cover the remainder of the card. Type up names on the computer in red and cut out each name. Place the name on the top of the place card. Each card should be placed on the guest table by each place setting.

♥ *How to Make the Teapot Centerpiece*
Yield: 1 teapot centerpiece

1 teapot
1 styrofoam ball
1 teapot shaped card on a stick (cut in half to fit the top of the teapot)
13 red foiled wrapped hearts
2 velvet hearts
1 queen of hearts playing card
1 king of hearts playing card
1 package rhinestone flourish (optional)
Glue stick
Hot glue

Cut the styrofoam ball in half. Place styrofoam ball into the mouth of the teapot with the flat side up. Place the stick with teapot card into the center of the styrofoam. Hot glue the foiled hearts on top of the styrofoam on each side of the teapot and one on the center on top (both front and back of the teapot card). Hot glue a queen of hearts card on the front of the teapot and a king of hearts on the back of the teapot. Cut out the velvet hearts. Glue the rhinestone pattern onto the card and velvet heart. Hot glue a velvet heart to the teapot, both front and back.

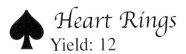

Heart Rings
Yield: 12

1 package heart glitter rings

Purchase rings at a cake decorating shop or a party store. Place one ring per guest at each place setting.

Card Design Candy Favors
Yield: 40 favors

1-6 ounce package card design candy favors

Place favors on each side of the two reindeers.

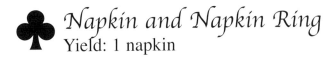

Napkin and Napkin Ring
Yield: 1 napkin

1-12x12 napkin
1 wooden napkin ring with heart decoration

Fold napkin in half and then into thirds. Hot glue a wooden red heart onto the napkin ring and place napkin though the middle of the ring. Fan out the top and bottom of the napkin.

The napkin goes on which side of the plate?
1. left
2. right
3. center of the plate

answer is left

Remember to put your napkin on your lap after being seated and place the napkin ring back to the left of your plate or slightly above.

Why is it good manners to send a thank you note to the person hosting the party?

1. To let the host or hostess know how much you appreciated being invited to the party.
2. To thank the host or hostess for having an enjoyable time.
3. Write a thank you note because it is good manners and the proper thing to do.
4. All the above

The answer is all the above

Dear Miss Lacey,
Thank you for inviting me to the party. It was very fun. I liked all the food and ringing the bells.

Sincerely,
David

Dear Miss Lacey,
Thank you for inviting me to the tea party. I had an amazing time. Thank you for the pretty red cape, the treats, the funny book and for letting me take home some cake. The food was very delicious.

Sincerely,
Annmarie

Games for the Holiday Tea for the Queen and King and Royal Family

The Queen's Favorite Card Game

For 2 or 3 Players:

Using the 10's, Jacks, Queens, Kings, Aces and two jokers from 2 decks of regular playing cards (total of 42 cards). Deal out all the cards, face down, to each player. In turn, each player turns over a top card from his/her face-down stack. Player displaying a Queen or Joker keeps the cards from that play, stacking them, face up by his/her side. In case two or three players display a Queen or Joker on the same play, players keep turning over (in turn) next card from his/her face-down pile until one player plays a Queen or Joker. If all face down cards are run through with no additional Queen or Joker coming into play, the displayed cards in the pot are dead and no player may claim them. Winner is the player with the most cards collected in his/her face-up pile.

To play with 4: omit the jokers. Each person receives 10 cards. Use 2 decks of cards. (40 total).

The guests also rang bells and sang songs while Miss Lacey played her accordion.

"For He is a Jolly good Fellow"
"Kumbaya"
"Grandfather's Clock" (The students made clicking sounds for ticking of the clock)
"When the Saints Go Marching In"
"Michael, Row the Boat Ashore"
"He's Got the Whole World in His Hands"

Miss Lacey also enjoyed seeing the faces of the children with they saw her surprise castle cake. Miss Lacey asked the students if anyone knew how many gold fish were around the castle cake. Eight year old David counted one line of fish across and one line down and then multiplied the two numbers together to come up with the answer. Miss Lacey was very impressed with David's answer.

Miss Lacey received many compliments on her tea party from families. The day after the tea she received a phone call from Abbey's grandmother and said that Abbey fell asleep with a big smile. She wore her cape and crown to bed. She added that her only regret was that she didn't get a picture of her granddaughter.

Miss Lacey said at the next tea club meeting they would learn about the legend of how tea originated.

The Legend of How Tea Originated

Hearsay states that the drinking of tea began in 2737 B.C. Emperor Shen Nong was traveling and became very weary. He decided to rest along the roadside. Due to hygiene, servants boiled water before any person could drink a beverage. It is said that some dried leaves fell into the boiling water and created a brownish liquid. The emperor enjoyed the taste and flavor of the beverage and thought it was very interesting. The servants made more. People believed that is how tea drinking came into existence.

A Short Summary of the History of Tea in China, Japan and Europe

The history of tea in China is complex. Tea was used in China for various ailments. The nobility drank tea as a status symbol and the common folks just enjoyed the flavor of tea.

The Chinese dictionary shows that tea drinking is dated back as far as the 3rd century. Chinese records show that China has the earliest records of tea drinking. The Tang Dynasty in 618 states that tea was a drink for social occasions. Tea leaves were processed into compressed shaped forms. They were called brick tea. All through the years steaming tea was the main method for making tea. However, in the 13th century China learned to roast tea leaves rather than to steam them.

In China tea became wide spread throughout the entire country. In 800 Lu Yu wrote a book on tea called the "Cha Chung". Eventually his form of tea service got to Zen Buddhist missionaries and then came to Imperial Japan.

Buddhist Priest Yesei brought tea seeds from China to Japan. He used tea as a form of religious meditation. He became known as the Father of tea in Japan. There were tea ceremonies which took hours of training. The tea ceremony became an art. It was not just how to make a cup of tea. One must learn to be polite, gracious and use most charming manners. Eventually, tea houses opened and everyone became involved and excited about tea.

Tea made its way to Europe by the Jesuit Father Jasper de Cruz in 1560. He was a Portuguese Jesuit. Once tea was introduced in Portugal, tea was shipped to Lisbon. France, Holland and Baltic countries received tea through transportation via the Dutch ships.

The cost of the tea was about $100.00 dollars per pound due to the ship's costs and travel time. Only the wealthy could drink tea. In the mid 1600's it became less costly and one could purchase tea in food shops in Holland and France. Everyone took some time out of their day to drink tea. Tea became popular in taverns in their gardens and served in portable tea sets.

The History of Tea in England

England learned about tea in 1652. It replaced the national drink ale. Just like the other countries, the nobility approved tea drinking. Even though tea prices were very high, tea mania spread throughout England.

It has been stated that Catherine of Braganza of Portugal grew up enjoying tea. She came to England to marry Charles II in 1662. She brought with her a casket of tea. She was called the tea–drinking queen.

Tea became the main beverage for breakfast and dinner. It was Anna, the Dutchess of Bedford (1788-1861) (called Lady Bedford) of England that introduced tea at time known as an afternoon meal. It is said that she became hungry in the middle of the afternoon. She would have one of her servants sneak her some tea. In addition she would look for a menu that would satisfy her hunger. At first she had tea time alone. However, eventually she began to invite friends for tea at the Belvoir Castle with a menu of tiny tea sandwiches, scones, small cakes and sweets. Other additional foods such as crumpets, thin crustless bread sandwiches and shrimp and fish pates were served on beautiful china and tea in a silver service set to make a most pleasant experience. It became so popular that it spread throughout England. She also enjoyed walking her guests through her fields at an afternoon tea. Garden teas were held by Lady Bedford. The practice became so popular that other social hostesses picked up on inviting friends to share an afternoon tea.

In this era the high and low tea service came into existence. The wealthy aristocrats served low teas. A low tea menu was served on the low coffee table in the parlor or garden and hence received its name. The menu consisted of simple gourmet tidbits in place of regular meals. Every person attending the low tea was encouraged to engage in good conversation and excellent presentation.

On the other hand, a high tea was considered the main meal of the day with a menu of various meats, vegetables and tea. The meal was served on a high table and thus called a high tea. High and low teas are often confused. Hotels in modern times call teas high teas. Miss Lacey said that she attended a high tea on Victoria Island at the Emperor's Hotel. It was very elegant with butler passed mini appetizers, finger sandwiches and dainty sweets all served with tea, of course. The orchestra played background music throughout the entire tea time. The tea usually took place from 2-4 p.m. or mid-afternoon. She told the students it was a wonderful and memorable experience.

Other English aristocrats had tea time in their gardens. They were entertained by orchestras, concerts and games. What once was known as teas for the idle rich allowed women to socialize freely without social criticism. All classes were welcomed whether being middle class or in British Society. It was wonderful to see both classes gathering freely for an afternoon tea.

Expected Etiquette at a Tea Party Gathering in England

When first meeting guests, there was a handshake. When sitting down, if carrying a purse, it was placed behind the chair. When sitting down, a napkin was placed on the person's lap. If the person left the chair, the napkin was placed on the chair and when the person returned, the napkin again was placed on their lap.

Sugar was always placed in the tea cup first, a thin slice of lemon on the side and then tea. The milk was then poured into the tea upon request.

A scone would be eaten first and eaten very neatly with fingers. The sweets were eaten after the scones. The person would always put clotted cream on each bite of scone and continue to it eat very neatly with their fingers. The spoon always went behind the cup of tea and one never left the spoon in the cup. The guest was required to look into the teacup when drinking.

What is Clotted Cream?

1. Made from cow's milk using steam
2. A thick cream
3. Used on scones at a tea
4. It is a nutty cooked milk
5. All of above

The amswer is: all of the above

English Garden Tea Party

Iced Tea and Tea Bags

Ice tea came about in 1904 at the World's Fair in St. Louis, Missouri in the U.S.A. when an Englishman, named Richard Blechynden, decided to give every person attending the fair a taste of his hot tea. Unfortunately, it turned out to be a very hot day. He dumped a big bag of ice into the hot tea and thus invented the world's first iced tea.

In 1908 Thomas Sullivan of New York made the first tea bag for restaurants. He wanted to help restaurants keep their kitchens tidy when brewing big batches of tea.

Types of Teas

A fine black tea is an *English breakfast tea*. Lemon can be served with hot tea if milk is not used. Do not serve milk and lemon together in tea. The milk will make the tea taste too tart or lemon can curdle the milk. *Irish breakfast tea* is stronger tea which is a favorite of many tea drinkers.

Usually breakfast tea is only served in the morning with one exception. The Irish drink it all day long. *Breakfast tea* is served with sugar and milk but never cream.

We have already discussed the *caravan tea*. It is a blend of *India and China black teas*. Sugar and milk is also served in this style of tea.

Earl Grey tea is well known and named after him. It has a smoky flavor and a hint of sweetness. *Earl Grey tea* is served plain and is a very popular tea in the world today.

Darjeeling tea is grown in India. It has a light flavor of muscatel. It is often served in the afternoon plain, but lemon is also offered, never milk.

Oolong tea was originally grown in China and imported to England in 1869. It is known as the Champagne of teas. It is a cross between black and green teas which gives the tea a fruity taste. *Oolong tea* is perfect for an afternoon tea with finger sandwiches and miniature cakes.

Japan used *green tea* for their tea service and it is considered a strong herbal tea. Japanese usually served green tea in the afternoon. *Herbal tea* is considered very healthy.

Keemun tea is a famous Chinese tea. It has a wine like taste similar to burgundy wine. Milk and sugar maybe be added to the *Keemuni tea*, but never lemon. It will make the tea taste too tart. Miss Lacey said that the Chinese drink tea from a small cup with no handle. Be sure to check out her display to see the different styles of tea sets. (See picture on page 6)

Chai is a high-grown Indian black tea mix with spices. The word Chai means tea in Hindi. Indian spiced Chai is often referred to as *Masala Chai.* This very expensive tea can be ordered on line.

Tea Choices Served to The World Tea Club:

Earl Grey Green Tea

Orange and Spice Herbal Tea

Black Tea-Tropical Peach Tea

Spiced Chai Tea

Cinnamon Apple Herbal Tea

Miss Lacey boiled water and laid out a variety of tea bags ready for the 5th graders to taste a flavored tea. Each of the students picked out a tea. They told her if they liked or disliked the taste of tea and why. They also discussed not only the flavor but also the aroma of the tea. She then prepared them for the American Heritage Tea Party in honor of Presidents Day. They would be doing the tea for 8 second graders. Miss Lacey made all the costumes and decorations for this festive and informative tea. She also added that she would assign a volunteer to serve for this particular tea.

An American Heritage Tea

The History of the Formation of America and Tea

The Pilgrims left England in August of 1620 with the hope of coming to America to start a new life. They wanted to have the freedom of religious rights. They sailed on the Mayflower from Plymouth, England and landed on Plymouth Rock in Massachusetts after 66 days at sea.

Tea was for sale in America in 1690 when New York City opened the first tea garden.

Colonial women enjoyed tea in 1720. During this time Americans rebelled against imported British tea due to the heavy tax. Some tea was being smuggled in from other places to avoid the high British tax. Tea companies became angry due to their diminishing profits. They insisted that parliament take action. Because Britain insisted on keeping the tax, the colonists became angry.

The British counted on the tea lovers in the colonies to pay the high tax, but it backfired. The colonial women refused to buy British tea. Finally, as hostility continued to grow in the colonies, men dressed up like Indians, gathered and threw hundreds of pounds of British tea into the Boston Harbor. This became known as the Boston Tea Party. America stabilized her government and her borders for her tea interests.

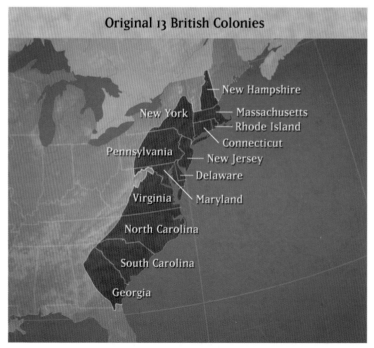

Original 13 British Colonies

New Hampshire
New York
Massachusetts
Rhode Island
Connecticut
Pennsylvania
New Jersey
Delaware
Virginia
Maryland
North Carolina
South Carolina
Georgia

Tea Time in America

Afternoon teas began to spring up in America. Americans began to select healthier teas such as herbal or English style tea. Many teas were served in the morning and also in the afternoon.

The First Flag in America and the Story About Betsy Ross

Betsy Ross was a seamstress and designed the first flag of the original 13 colonies. Betsy Ross and George Washington had a meeting on how to make the American flag. She made it clear that the flag should be designed using common motifs of an alternating red and white striped field with white stars in a blue canton, George Washington thought that she should make 6 points to each star. She disagreed and said that the 5 pointed star is best using uneven versus even number points. She could save material and it would look much nicer. So, after a little friendly persuasion, he agreed to making the 5 pointed stars. Betsy Ross designed the flag during the American Revolution which featured 13 stars to represent the original colonies and arranged in a circle. Also there were 7 red and 6 white stripes with a total of 13. Thus the first flag was born in the spirit of 1776 with great pride. Today the United States flag still has the 13 strips to represent the first 13 colonies.

How many stars are on the United States Flag today?
1. 33
2. 49
3. 50

The answer is 3

Which two states were last added to the United States?
1. California and Florida
2. Alaska and Hawaii
3. Alabama and Georgia

The answer is 2

George Washington was the first president of the United States. He firmly believed that he should serve his country and did not take any pay while running the country as president.

Martha Washington often gave afternoon teas to various important guests and she always wore a mop cap decorated with lace and a lacey shawl. It is said that she was the first lady that made this fashionable style so famous. She never went anywhere without wearing her mop cap or shawl. The reason that most women wore a mop cap was due to the dust in the air from the wide open spaces and also due to the lack of infrequent bathing and lack of washing hair. Modern day plumbing was not installed in homes nor running water or toilets as we know it today.

Martha Washington enjoyed entertaining guests in their Colonial home sometimes in the afternoon offering tea and finger sandwiches and bite size desserts. She planned for several days to have a tea for honored guests to show off the new flag designed by Betsy Ross. She was not sure if the President would attend due to his busy schedule. Nevertheless, she decided to invite the following guests for tea. Abigail Adams, Betsy Ross, Martha Jefferson, and her daughters Mary Wayles (called Polly), Ana and the Indian maiden, Morning Star, for a memorable tea and a delightful afternoon.

The American Heritage Tea Menu

Presented by Martha Washington

Martha Washington's Tea Sandwiches

Independence Cherry Scones

Valley Forge Strawberries

President Washington's Mini Cherry Cheesecakes

Mini Revolutionary Red Velvet Cupcakes

Colonial Tea

Martha Washington's Tea Sandwiches
Yield: 16 whole sandwiches

1-16 ounce can prepared cream cheese frosting
2-8 ounce (each) cream cheese, softened
$^1/_2$ cup finely chopped pecans (optional)
1-10 ounce bag julienne-cut carrots, chopped
2-1 pound loaves cinnamon raisin bread
silk rose petals

In a five quart mixing bowl, mix together cream cheese frosting, cream cheese, pecans and carrots. Spread one side of each piece of bread with the carrot/frosting mixture. Top with remaining bread slice. Using a sharp long bread knife, cut the crust from each sandwich. Cut the sandwiches in half diagonally and then cut in half again. Two whole sandwiches make 4 halves or 8 fourths.

When making sandwiches ahead of time, keep them from drying out by covering them loosely with a sheet of wax paper. Place a damp kitchen cloth over the wax paper. Placing a damp cloth directly over the sandwiches will make them soggy. Refrigerate until 15 minutes before serving. Garnish with rose petals.

Independence Cherry Scones
Yield: 16 scones

1 large egg
1 teaspoon vanilla
$^1/_2$ cup whipping cream
2 cups flour plus more for dusting the board
$^1/_4$ cup sugar
2 teaspoons baking powder
$^1/_4$ teaspoon salt
6 tablespoons unsalted butter
  cut into pieces and well chilled
$^2/_3$ cup dried cherries
parchment paper
1 package 50 star picks

Egg Wash
1 egg
2 tablespoons milk
granulated sugar

continued on next page

Preheat oven to 425F. Cover baking sheet with a sheet of parchment paper to prevent the bottom of the scones from burning. Mix together the 1 egg, vanilla and whipping cream in a small bowl. In a food processor, add 2 cups flour, sugar, baking powder and salt. Pulse a few times to mix. Add butter and process until the mixture forms coarse meal. Add egg mixture and pulse until a crumbly dough. Turn dough out onto floured surface and sprinkle dried cherries over dough. Briefly knead and flatten to a $3/4$ inch thick round. Cut into wedges or use a scalloped round biscuit cutter to cut out each scone. Beat egg and milk together. Brush egg wash over the top of each scone. Sprinkle the granulated sugar over each scone. Bake for about 13 minutes. Cool slightly. Remove scones from the baking sheet and place onto cooling racks. Place scones on a tray lined with a doily.

★ *Valley Forge Strawberries*
Yield: 1-12 inch Footed Serving Tray

4-1 pound containers of strawberries
1-12 inch doily

Leaving hulls on the strawberries, wash and dry them thoroughly.
Starting from the outside of a footed platter, arrange strawberries in a circle with the hull side up.
Continue to make a second, third and middle center row. Place strawberries on the top of the second row and continue until all the strawberries are arranged. Cover until serving time.

★ *President Washington's Cherry Cheesecakes*
Yield: 48 cheesecakes

1-12 ounce package vanilla wafers
2-8 ounce (each) packages cream cheese
$3/4$ cup white sugar
2 eggs
1 teaspoon vanilla
1-21 ounce can cherry pie filling

Preheat oven to 350F. Line miniature muffin tins with miniature paper liners. Place one vanilla wafer into each paper liner. In a mixing bowl, beat cream cheese, sugar, eggs and vanilla until light and fluffy. Fill each miniature muffin liner with this mixture almost to the top. Place one pie filling cherry per cheesecake. Bake for 15 minutes. Cool. Place on a tiered tray.

Mini Revolutionary Red Velvet Cupcakes
Yield: 24 cupcakes

2-10 ounce packages (each) red velvet mini cupcakes
1 doily
1 footed tray
2 packages (each) patriotic icing decorations (12 count)

Place cupcakes on a footed tray lined with a red doily. Decorate with one patriotic decoration in the center of each cupcake. Cover with plastic wrap until serving time.

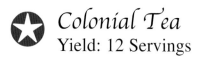 # Colonial Tea
Yield: 12 Servings

3 lemon tea bags
3 herbal peppermint tea bags
3 perfect peach tea bags
3 Earl Gray tea bags
3 Green Tea bags
1 tray lined with a doily or
1 basket lined with a napkin
3 lemons, cut into wedges
24 sugar cubes
two tea pots of hot water
milk

Place tea bags onto a separate tray lined with doily or a basket lined with a napkin. Arrange tea bags. Cut lemons into wedges. Arrange the sugar cubes on the tray or a sugar server. Place milk into the creamer. Boil the water and pour into the warmed teapots. Let each guest select the flavor of tea. Pour hot water into individual cups and place a tea bag into each cup. Let the tea steep a few minutes in the cup. Serve with lemon wedges and sugar. Remember, do not use lemons when using milk for sometimes the milk will curdle or make the tea taste too tart.

Legend that George Washington Chopped Down a Cherry Tree

Miss Lacey said that one of the reasons for serving tea items with cherries was due to the legend that George Washington chopped down a cherry tree at age 6. She explained to the club that the story goes that he loved his hatchet. He went about the orchard chopping everything in his way to amuse himself. One day he spotted an English cherry tree and took the edge of his hatchet to the bark of his father's favorite cherry tree. Eventually the tree died. His father questioned George asking him, "do you know who killed my cherry tree." At that point George began to cry. "I cannot tell a lie, father. I cut the cherry tree bark with my hatchet." The anger on George's father's face turned to it is alright. He let George know that he was very proud of him for telling him the truth. He learned that "honesty is the best policy".

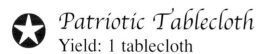 ## Patriotic Tablecloth
Yield: 1 tablecloth

1 purchased tablecloth or material to make a tablecloth
surging thread or a spool of thread

Surge the edges of the material to form a rolled hem or turn
over each end ¼ inch twice and stitch to form a narrow hem. Cover the table the day of the tea.

Heritage Napkins
Yield: 8 napkins

3¹/₂ yards red material
3³/₄ yards of 2¹/₂ inch wide white lace
white thread
red surging thread
8 teapot napkin rings or napkin rings of choice

Purchase napkins or buy 3¹/₂ yards red material and cut each napkin to the size of 15x15 inch square. Surge the edges on all four sides of the napkin to form a rolled hem or turn over each end ¹/₄ inch twice on all four sides and stitch to form a narrow hem. Cut 15¹/₂ inches of lace for each napkin. Turn each edge of the lace over ¹/₄ inch and stitch with white thread. Stitch lace across the top of each napkin. Fold napkin in half with lace at the top of the napkin. Fold napkin again into thirds. Starting at the opposite end of the lace, place napkin through the hole of the napkin ring. Fan out the bottom of the red napkin. Place to the left of each place setting for each guest. To remove the napkin from the napkin ring, slide the napkin ring down the napkin (away from the lace) and off the napkin. Set the napkin ring down on the left side or slightly above the place setting. Unfold the napkin and place the napkin on your lap after being seated.

A Patriotic Gift with Name Place Setting
Yield: 8 gifts name place settings

8 square pint milk cartons, (each) 12 inches around the
   bottom of each milk carton
1 roll pink crepe paper
1 roll red, white and blue crepe paper
8 styrofoam balls (4 inches in diameter)
1 name tag (front and back)
1-25 foot party decorative star garland
1 package Krinkle Shred®
1 package red, silver and blue star picks
1 package flag toothpicks
4 bouquets of red and blue silk carnations with
   green leaves
1 package red, silver and blue star picks
   (one for front and back)

continued on next page

¹/₂ inch wide clear tape
glue stick
hot glue gun

Cut each milk carton down to 3 inches high. Wrap the pink crepe paper around the entire carton and tape in place. Repeat with the red, white and blue crepe paper to cover the pink crepe paper. Cut 3-13 inch strips of red, white and blue crepe paper. Wrap around the diameter of the styrofoam ball in three sections to cover most of the ball. Set aside. Type up each person's name twice on the computer. Using craft pinking shears, cut out the names and glue onto the center front and back of the decorated milk carton. Wrap three rows of decorative star garland around the bottom of the milk carton, twist ends together and hot glue in place. Fill the carton with the Krinkle Shred® (and also with some of the Krinkle Shred® sticking out over the top of the milk carton). Place one star pick into the top center of the ball and one flag toothpick on each side of the star. Using 8 carnations, alternate the red, white and blue carnations around the top side of the decorated styrofoam ball forming a circle of carnations. Place one sprig of green leaves with one or two carnations into the Krinkle Shred® on the right hand side corner of the carton. Hot glue the decorated styrofoam ball onto the Krinkle Shred® and inside the edges of the milk carton. Center one gift above the plate at each place setting.

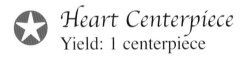 ## Heart Centerpiece
Yield: 1 centerpiece

1 heart shape vase with 2 glass test tubes
1 bouquet red, white and blue carnations
2 gold ribbons (each) ¹/₂ wide and 16 inches long
   (with wire edges)
1-8 inch place mat circle
³/₄ yard ³/₄ inch of gold and white lace

Cut apart the one bouquet of flowers to make two bouquets. Cut the end of one bouquet to be shorter than the other bouquet. Insert each bouquet into a test tube. Place the taller bouquet into the left side of the vase and the shorter bouquet into the right side. Wrap the gold ribbon around the top of each test tube and tie into a knot. Bend ribbon into 1-2 inch increments to add some decorative dimension. Stitch lace onto the edge of the place mat circle. Place centerpiece in the center of the table on the place mat circle.

⭐ *Martha Washington's Mop Cap*
Yield: one Mop Cap

1 sailor hat
1-18 inches wide x 44 inches long silver organza material
 or purchase a cap at a costume shop
1 yard gold trim with wire edges, 2 inches wide
white thread

Fold down the edge of the sailor hat. Even the top of the hat. Place the silver material over the entire sailor hat with edges inside the hat. Stitch the silver edges around the inside bottom of the cap. Gather the gold trim and stitch around the outside bottom of the mop cap.

⭐ *Martha Washington's Shawl*
Yield: 1 shawl

30 inches long x 44 inches wide silver organza material
1¹/₂ yards gold ribbon with wire edges (2 inches wide)
1¹/₂ yards white braid trim (¹/₄ inch wide)
white thread
1 butterfly pin (purchase or make one)
1 pin back
hot glue

Turn over edges of the material ¹/₄ inch twice and stitch to hide the raw edges. Fold the material into a triangle. Gather the gold ribbon lace and stich along the folded edge of the triangle. Stitch the white braid over the edge of the gold ribbon lace. Hot glue pin back to the back center of the butterfly. Place the shawl around the child and pin the shawl closed with the butterfly pin.

Other Costumes made like Martha Washington's mop cap and shawls

Martha Jefferson wears a lace mop cap in red with white lace overlay on a red velvet shawl. The neckline edges are trimmed with white lace.

Betsey Ross's gold lace shawl is trimmed with red ribbon. She wears a star crown adorned with ribbon and a flag pick in the center of the bow. Her cape is trimmed with red ribbon and held closed with a paper star crown pin to match her hat.

Abigail Adams is in a blue organza shawl held together with a pearl pin. Her blue organza mop cap is trimmed with white lace.

 ## Ana's Hat
Yield: 1 hat

1-15 inch round straw deep blue place mat
$1^1/_3$ yards white trim ($^1/_2$ inch wide)
$1^3/_4$ yards decorative trim ($1^1/_4$ inches wide)
13 inches white trim (1 inch wide)
2-20 inch (each) ribbons ($^1/_4$ inch wide) used for ties
1 wooden red heart
2 American flag toothpicks
8-$^3/_4$ inch gold foiled wrapped coins
1-1 inch gold foiled wrapped coin
6 mini stars with red, white and blue
1 mini red star
white thread
hot glue

Lay the place mat flat on the cutting table. Measure and mark a straight line 7 inches in length from the edge up to the center bottom of the place mat, stitch about $^1/_4$ inch on one side of the line bringing the stitching to a point at the top of the 7 inch line and then pivot to stitch down the opposite side of the line approximately

continue on next page

$^1/_4$ inch out. Cut through the marked line to make the back of the hat. Starting on the back, sew the white trim around the edge of the seam of the placement. Sew a second row of blue decorative trim above the white trim. Starting at the bottom of the back opening, sew lace on the edge of each side remembering to pivot at the top of the opening slit. Fold the left slit over to the right side. Tack in place. Glue the heart onto the front center of the hat. Break off the picks from the flags. Glue a flag at the top of the heart on an angle on each side. Glue one $^1/_4$ inch foiled wrapped coin on the heart just below the flags. Place the one inch gold foiled wrapped coin in the middle of the crown. In an inverted horseshoe fashion, place the remaining foiled gold coins around the top of the crown. Place 3 red, white and blue stars at the top of the heart, with one in the center and the other two on each side of the star. Center the ties on each side of the hat and stitch in place.

 ## Ana's Shoulder Scarf
Yield: 1 Scarf

1 piece silver color organza (1 yard long x 12 inches wide)
1 yard gold and white lace (1 inch wide)
1 yard red, white and blue braid trim ($^1/_4$ inch wide)
white thread

Turn over edges of the organza material $^1/_4$ inch twice and stitch to hide the raw edges. At the top of the organza fabric seam, sew on the lace and then the braid over the top of the lace.

 ## Patriotic Pin for Ana's Scarf
Yield: 1 pin

1 crown decoration
1 star on a pick
2 American flag toothpicks
1 pin back
hot glue

Glue the star pick onto the center back of the crown decoration. Hot glue a flag toothpick on the back of the crown on each side of the star. Hot glue the pin on the center middle of the back of the crown decoration.

Polly's Hat
Yield: 1 hat

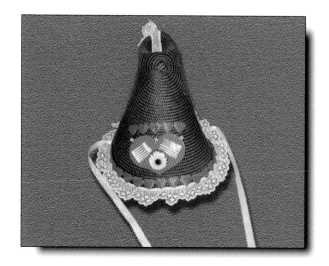

1-15 inch round dark blue straw place mat
white thread
1$^1/_3$ yards white lace (1 inch wide)
1 yard red heart trim
1 wooden heart
2 American flag toothpicks
3 mini red, white and blue stars
1 mini red star
1 foiled wrapped flower decorated round candy
2-20 inch (each) ribbons ($^1/_4$ inch wide) for ties
red thread

Lay the place mat flat on the cutting table. Measure and mark a straight line 7 inches long from the bottom to the center of the place mat. Starting at the bottom of the place mat, stitch about $^1/_4$ inch out from one side of the line bringing the stitch at a point at the top of the 7 inch line. Pivot to stitch down the opposite side, approximately $^1/_4$ inch away from the line. Cut through the marked line to make the back of the hat. Sew lace trim around the bottom of the place mat. Starting at the bottom of the opening of the hat, sew the white trim all the way around the edge of the seam opening. Make an indentation in the top back opening to form a dip like tiny crown in the hat. Sew the back seams together from the bottom (5 inches up) to form the hat. At random and using the red thread, tack on the red hearts around the diameter of the hat positioned just above the lace. Follow directions for heart pin for Polly's scarf (page 67) for the heart decoration on the hat. Center the ties on each side of the hat and stitch in place.

Polly's Shoulder Scarf
Yield: 1 scarf

1 piece cotton patriotic material (44-48 inches long x 15 inches wide)
1 piece of off white lace (44-48 inches long x 1 inch wide)
white thread

Turn over edges of the material $^1/_4$ inch twice on all four sides and stitch to hide the raw edges. Stitch lace across the top of the scarf.

⭐ Heart Pin for Poly's Scarf
Yield: 1 pin

1 red wooden heart
1 blue star on a pick
1 mini red star
2 American flag toothpicks
1 round chocolate foiled wrapped candy
1 pin back
hot glue
hot glue gun

Remove the pick from the star and hot glue the mini star onto the middle of the larger blue star. Hot glue the star at the top of the heart. Break off the picks on each of the flag toothpicks. At an angled position, hot glue one flag on right and left side of the heart. Glue the foiled candy over the bottom center of the flags. Glue the pin back onto the center back of the heart. Use the heart pin to fasten the scarf and also as a decoration.

⭐ Morning Star's Indian Cape
Yield: 1 cape

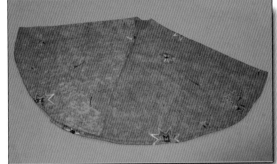

1 yard Indian print material
1 cape pattern
thread
1 large snap

Using the pattern, cut out the cape. Turn over edges of the material ¹/₄ inch twice and stitch to hide the raw edges. Sew on snap which is used to fasten the cape.

⭐ Indian Band and Necklace
Yield: 1 Band and Necklace

1 kit with Indian band and feathers
1 head band strip (15 inches long x 2 inches wide), optional
1 star, optional

Cut a strip of material used from making the cape. Turn edges over once on top and bottom of the band and stitch down in place so that

continued on next page

the cape and head band match. Carefully, cut out a star from leftover Indian patterned material. Stitch the star onto the center of the head band by sewing down through the middle of the star. The ready-made necklace has a tie and it is simply tied in the back of the neck and dangles down over the cape.

 ## George Washington Attire
Yield: 1 disguise kit

1 George Washington instant disguised kit

Each kit has a wig and the ruffle tie scarf.

 ## Tea Server's Patriotic Top Hat
Yield: 1 patriotic hat

1 American flag toothpick
1 patriotic top hat
1 plastic 4x4 inch red star candy dish
hot glue

Break off the toothpick from the flag. Glue the flag into the middle of the star candy dish. Glue star candy dish to the front of the hat.

 ## Tea Server's Bow Tie
Yield: 1 bow tie

1 black bow tie
2 mini red stars
1 red star pick
hot glue
glue gun

Glue large red star in the middle of the bow tie.
Glue mini red stars, one on each side of the large star.

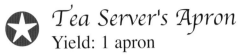 *Tea Server's Apron*
Yield: 1 apron

Purchase an apron with stars or a patriotic theme.
(See tea server's apron on page 77).

 *A Patriotic No Sew Tea Hat*
Yield: one hat

1-15 inch round blue place mat
3 plastic flowers (2 red and one white)
1 silver color star pick
1-12 inch long x ½ inch flexible tin band (optional)
3 mini red, white and blue stars, (optional)
Hot Glue

Cut out a 6 inch circle in diameter from the middle of the place mat. Cut the place mat from bottom to the opening. Overlap the two pieces of the place mat and glue together to form the hat. Alternating the red with the white flowers in the middle, glue on the three flowers over and across the glued seam. Break off pick on the silver star. Glue the onto star onto the hat below the white flower. Starting at the end of the red flower to the left, weave the tin up and down and around the star towards the flower on the right. Glue on one star to three separate petals of the white flower.

★★★★★★★★★★★★★★★★★★★★★★★★★★

A Summary of Thank You Notes from the Students That Attended the American Heritage Tea

They all agreed that the food was delicious and that they had learned a lot about American history, tea parties and how to properly hold a tea cup. They appreciated being served by one of the male club members and agreed it was a fun experience. Every student said thank you in their own way, expressing something special they enjoyed at this great Heritage Tea Party.

Sincerely,
The Second Grade Class.

★★★★★★★★★★★★★★★★★★★★★★★★★★

Miss Lacey Visits the 2nd Grade Class

She made the tea party outfits for the Heritage Tea Party and decided to have the students try on their tea party costumes one week before the tea to be sure they would fit. She took pictures to see the end results.

It is a perfect fit!

George Washington

Martha Washington

Abigail Adams

Martha Jefferson

Betsy Ross

Polly

Ana

Morning Star

Tea Guests At The Party

Abigail visits with Martha Washington at the party, as Morning Star looks on.

Guest Ana

Martha Washington, George Washington and Betsy Ross holding the colonial flag, the first flag of America.

Guests: Martha Jefferson, Morning Star and Abigail Adams

Guests: Betsy Ross, Polly and Ana

Martha Jefferson and Morning Star

Good Etiquette/Table Manners At The Tea

Martha Jefferson is seated by her gift place setting as she listens to Morning Star.

Betsy Ross is sliding her napkin through the napkin ring.

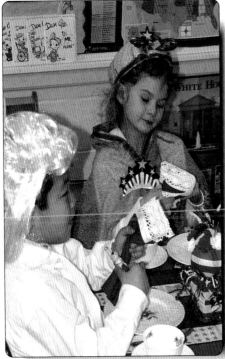

George Washington and Betsy Ross are taking the napkin rings off their napkins.

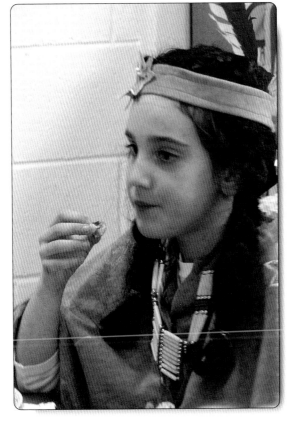

Morning Star is chewing with her mouth close and one hand in her lap.

75

Our Stars at the American Heritage Tea

A Short History of Tea in France

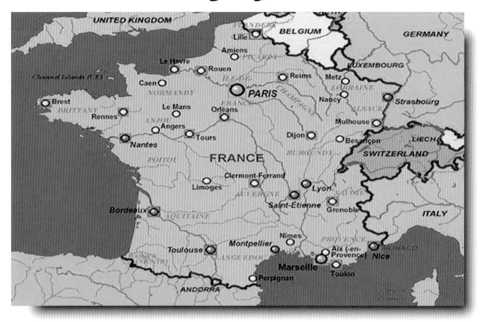

At the club meeting Miss Lacey said that they would be discussing a short history of tea in France and also make plans for the last tea party for the school year.

When we think of France, we generally think of coffee as the popular beverage. We paint a picture of a Frenchman with a black mustache, wearing a beret, enjoying the view of the Eiffel Tower, while drinking a cup of freshly brewed French roasted coffee. Most people don't think that the French could ever enjoy a cup of tea in a lovely tea room.

We often think that people from the United Kingdom are the tea drinkers. It is a big surprise to most people that France and the Netherlands were the two countries that imported the most tea. Long before England's Queen Victoria's reign (1837-1901) and afternoon teas, the French became acquainted with tea in 1636.

Tea was imported for medicinal purposes. Doctors believed that green tea could cure gout. The upper class could afford to eat excessive amounts of meat and thus came down with gout. King Louis XIV, known as the Sun King, drank a lot of tea each day to help cure his gout.

People began to recognize the good taste of tea despite the fact that doctors recommended it only for medicinal purposes. Tea was the upper class drink due to the cost. The rich drank tea during the French Revolution. Not everyone enjoyed drinking tea, and for the next 50 years tea drinking was definitely out of style.

Today people drink tea daily. There are 140 "salons de thes" in Paris alone. Many Bed and Breakfasts have tea service and also country villages and many cities in France serve tea. Never doubt that drinkers can visit France and chat over a hot cup of tea.

Bon Appetite!!!

Now that the club had a short history of tea in France, it was time for Miss Lacey to talk about the special tea party surprise. Miss Lacey explained that she had volunteered at the local humane society over the summer months. She fell in love with the cutest French poodle triplets. She always fussed over the trio poodles. When she heard they were up for adoption, she decided to sign the papers and bring them home. She had a new family and named her poodle darlings Dixie, Pixie and Trixie. She was very excited for her Club to meet them at the last tea of the year. She assured the students that there would be a very special surprise.

First, she wanted her club members to learn how to make doggie biscuits for the triplets and also practice how to make cucumber sandwiches. She handed out the recipes to the assigned club members and ask the members to wash their hands and get started.

Cucumber Sandwiches
Yield: 40 finger sandwiches

2-8 ounce packages (each) cream cheese
1 teaspoon Worcestershire sauce
1 teaspoon onion powder
1-1½ loaves (1 pound 8 ounce) wheat bread
2 cucumbers
dried dill weed
2 doilies
2-12 inch trays

Add Worcestershire sauce and onion powder to the cream cheese. Beat until smooth and creamy. Set aside. Using a 3 inch round cookie cutter, cut out the bread rounds. Spread each bread round with the cream cheese mixture. Leave the peelings on the cucumbers. Wash and dry each one. Run fork from top to bottom around the cucumber to make a decorative edge. Slice the cucumbers into circles. Lay each cucumber slice out on a paper towel and squeeze out the extra moisture. Place one cucumber slice on each bread round; sprinkle with dill weed. Arrange cucumber sandwiches on trays lined with a doily.

Miss Lacey explained that cucumber sandwiches are popular and are served throughout the entire world at tea parties.

Doggie Biscuits
Yield: 3 dozen

2 cups flour
2 cups whole wheat flour
³/₄ cup cornmeal
4 tablespoons vegetable oil
2 cups boiling water
4 chicken bouillon cubes

Combine the flour, whole wheat flour and cornmeal together. Stir in the oil and mix well. Dissolve bouillon cubes in boiling water. Add to the flour/cornmeal mixture. Mix to form a stiff dough. Roll out on a floured surface. Cut out with a dog bone cookie cutter. Bake at 300F for 30 minutes. Cool thoroughly. Store in an airtight container.

She told the club members she would let the triplets sample the dog bones and save the remaining supply for the poodle tea party.

Next, she showed the club members a picture of the guest table setup for the triplets and discussed the layout.

At the end of the club meeting, Kay raised her hand and said that she was going to have a poodle tea party for her family over the weekend. She wanted permission to bring in the pictures from the party at the next club meeting. Miss Lacey and the members thought it would be fun to see the pictures and also have Kay give a short summary about the tea party. Kay said that her Auntie Starrie was going to make the hats and also the food for the tea party.

A Poodle Tea Party for the Family

Poodle Tea Party for the Family Menu

Veggie Tea Sandwiches

Mini Quiches

Chocolate Covered Strawberries

Mini Cupcakes Decorated
with Dog Bone Candies

Dog Bone Sugar Cookies

Mini Cream Puffs

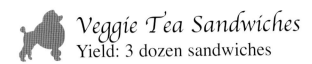

Veggie Tea Sandwiches
Yield: 3 dozen sandwiches

1-8 ounce can crescent rolls
1-8 ounce package cream cheese, softened
$\frac{1}{2}$ teaspoon Worcestershire sauce
$\frac{1}{2}$ pound broccoli, chopped and divided
1 pint grape tomatoes
1 doily

Carefully unroll the crescent roll dough. Place the entire sheet flat on ungreased cookie sheet. Make sure the crescent sheet holds its shape. Bake at 375F for 10 minutes. Cool slightly for about 1 minute. Loosen crescent sheet from cookie sheet. Cut each of the 8 triangles into 4-5 small triangle shapes and cool on cooling rack. Set aside. Beat cream cheese and blend in Worcestershire sauce. Spread a thin layer of cream cheese mixture over the top of each triangle. Wash and dry broccoli thoroughly. Remove stems. Chop the head of broccoli into tiny pieces. Sprinkle 1 teaspoon broccoli over each cream cheese triangle. Wash and dry the grape tomatoes. Make saw tooth cuts around the middle and through each tomato. Separate halves. Place one tomato flower in the center of each triangle finger sandwich. Place on an oblong tray lined with a doily. Refrigerate until serving time.

Mini Quiches
Yield: 36 mini quiches

Crust
1-3 ounce package cream cheese, softened
$\frac{1}{2}$ cup butter, softened
1 cup flour

Filling
4 eggs
1-8 ounce package cream cheese, softened
$\frac{1}{4}$ cup half and half or milk
$\frac{1}{2}$ teaspoon dehydrated onion
$\frac{1}{4}$ teaspoon Worcestershire sauce
$\frac{1}{4}$ teaspoon salt
$\frac{1}{8}$ teaspoon pepper
1 cup shredded Monterey Jack cheese, divided

continued on next page

83

baking spray
1 doily to fit the serving tray

In a mixing bowl, cream butter and cream cheese. Add flour; beat until well blended.Shaped dough into a ball. Roll out the dough on a floured counter top or pastry cover on a round board. Using a 3 inch round cookie cutter, cut out the individual crusts. Line each greased miniature muffin cup to form the shells for the mini quiches. Beat eggs and cream cheese mixture together. Add the half and half a little at a time and continue to beat. Add the onion, salt, pepper and Worcestershire sauce. Stir until blended together. Fill each crust with 2 teaspoons egg mixture. Sprinkle a rounded teaspoon of Monterey Jack cheese on top of each quiche. Bake at 400F for 10-12 minutes or until egg mixture is set and crusts are golden brown. Cool slightly. Remove the quiches from the pan and continue to cool thoroughly. Cover and refrigerate until day of the tea party. Place quiches on a microwavable dish and microwave for 1-2 minutes. Place quiches on a tray lined with a doily. Serve.

 ## *Chocolate Covered Strawberries*
Yield: approximately 24 strawberries

1 pound strawberries
1-7 ounce container dipping chocolate
1-8 inch doily
silk pink flowers
silk green leaves garnish

Leave the hulls on each strawberry. Wash off the strawberries and dry thoroughly with paper towel. Follow the package directions for melting chocolate in the microwave. Starting at the bottom of each strawberry, dip into the chocolate $2/3$ the way up exposing the top and hull of each strawberry. Place each strawberry on waxed paper and dry the chocolate strawberry. Place strawberries on a platter lined with a doily. Garnish with silk flowers and leaves. Cover and refrigerate until serving time.

Mini Cupcakes Decorated with Dog Bone Candies
Yield: approximately 90 mini cupcakes

1-18.25 ounce dark chocolate cake mix
eggs
oil
water
2-16 ounce cans (each) vanilla frosting
pink food coloring
1-8 ounce container pink jimmies
$^1/_3$ pound multi colored dog bone candies

Follow cake mix directions. Line each mini muffin cup with a mini cupcake liner. Using a 1 tablespoon portion control scoop, fill each lined muffin cup. Bake at 350F for 5-6 minutes or until toothpick inserted into the center of the cupcake comes out clean. Remove cupcakes from pan and cool thoroughly. Add 2 drops of the pink food coloring to the vanilla frosting. Using a number 28 star tip, pipe frosting on each cupcake. Dip each frosted cupcake face down into the pink jimmies. Place one dog bone candy standing up, in the center of each cupcake for a garnish. Arrange on a tray and cover until the party.

Dog Bone Sugar Cookies
Yield: combination of 30 large and small cookies

1 cup butter
1 cup sugar
2 eggs
1 teaspoon vanilla
1 teaspoon almond flavoring
2$^1/_2$ cups flour
1$^1/_2$ teaspoons baking powder
$^1/_2$ teaspoon salt
parchment paper
1-10 inch white doily

Glaze
1$^1/_2$ cup powdered sugar
3 tablespoons water
$^1/_2$ teaspoon almond flavoring
$^1/_2$ teaspoon salt
1 drop pink food coloring

continued on next page

85

Garnish
1-8 ounce container pink sanding sugar
1-16 ounce container vanilla frosting
pink food coloring
$\frac{1}{2}$ pound multi color dog bone candies

Preheat the oven to 350F. Cream butter and sugar together. Add eggs, vanilla and almond flavoring; beat. Add flour to the mixture, a little at a time, and continue to beat until dough is blended together. Sprinkle flour on work surface. Roll out the dough to about $\frac{1}{4}$ inch thick. Using a small size and also a larger size dog bone cookie cutter; cut out the dog bone cookies. Place on a cookie sheet lined with parchment paper. Bake at 350F for 10-12 minutes or until lightly golden brown on the bottom of each cookie. Cool. Make a glaze. In a separate bowl, mix water, almond flavoring and salt into the powdered sugar. Add the food coloring and beat thoroughly until smooth. Dip each dog bone cookie into the glaze and sprinkle with pink sanding sugar. Add two drops of pink food coloring to the vanilla frosting. Using a number 30 star tip, pipe on one star in the middle of each dog bone cookie. Place one dog bone candy, standing up, in the center of each star frosting. Some of the dog bone cookies do not have a dog bone garnish because some guests may not like hard candy. Place cookies on a platter lined with a doily. Cover until serving time.

 Mini Cream Puffs
Yield: 70 mini cream puffs

1-36.6 ounce box frozen,
    Belgian mini cream puffs
1-6 inch doily
3 pink silk flowers
6-8 silk rose petals
6 dog bone candies
1 small doily

Take out the amount of cream puffs needed and thaw. Place cream puffs on a small tray lined with a doily. Garnish with pink flowers, rose petals and dog bone candies. Cover and refrigerate until serving time.

Tablecloth
Auntie Starrie came to our house and measured the tablecloth for our dining room table. She used pink polka dot flannel with a white background for the underlay and a glitzy see through pink organza for the overlay tablecloth. The flannel material holds the organza overlay in place.

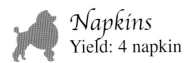 *Napkins*
Yield: 4 napkin

4-9x10 pink polka dot flannel material pieces
4-9x10 glitzy pink organza material pieces
pink thread

Place the organza on top of the pink polka dot flannel
and pin in place for each napkin. Turn over the edges
of the material twice $1/4$ inch and stitch the seam on all
four sides to cover raw edges of the material.

 Napkin Rings
Yield: 4 napkin rings

4 wooden napkin rings
4 poodle appliqués, (2x3 inches)
hot glue

Hot glue one poodle per napkin ring.

 How to Place Napkin Through the Napkin Ring
Yield: 4 napkins in napkin rings

Fold napkin to look like a fan. Place napkin through the napkin ring. Center the napkin ring in the middle of
the napkin to make the napkin look like a bow.

 Gift/Place Setting Names
Yield: 4 gift place setting names

4 mini wooden flower pots
1 can black spray paint
1 deep cardboard box
4 wooden round pieces (each) $1/2$ inch in diameter
1-2 inch styrofoam ball, divided
4-10 inch pink boa pieces, divided

continued on next page

Gift/Place Setting Names, continued

4 pink flowers, divided
4 planter markers, divided
24 dog bone candies, divided
2 yards pink ribbon, divided
1 package adhesive flower shapes
4 name tags, (one for each guest)
hot glue gun
glue stick

Place wooden flowerpots inside the cardboard box. Spray them black and let dry. Glue the bottom of the flowerpot onto the center of each of the wooden round pieces. Cut the styrofoam ball into 4 small pieces to fit inside of each flowerpot. Wrap the boa around the edge of each wooden piece, overlapping a couple inches, and glue in place. Glue one flower onto the front/bottom of the flowerpot. Stick one planter marker through the styrofoam in each pot. Glue 6 dog bone candies around the top of the styrofoam for each pot. Cut four 8 inch strips of ribbon. The one bow around the top of each stick is found underneath the planter marker. Place a small adhesive flower on top of the center knot of each bow and one at the top right hand corner of the planter marker. Make name tags (one for each guest). Using the glue stick, glue name tags on the center bottom of the planter markers. Place one for each person at their place setting.

 ## The Poodle Centerpiece
Yield: 1 centerpiece

1-14 inch round cake decorating board
1-16 inch round cake decorating board
2-6 foot feather boas
1 bouquet small pink flowers with leaves
1 Wilton Cupcake Bouquet® pot
6 ready-made cupcakes
2¼ yards pink ribbon
1-16 ounce can dark chocolate frosting
½ pound dog bone candies
1-2x3 inch poodle appliqué
hot glue
5 stuffed French poodle animals

continued on next page

88

Glue in place the boa around the outer edge of the 14 inch board. Glue 3 pink flowers onto the boa in the center front. Wrap the boa around the flower pot and glue in place. Wrap the ribbon around the center of the top rim of the flowerpot. Glue on the poodle appliqué in the center top of the flowerpot. Starting from the center left of the poodle rim, glue dog bones around to meet the tail of the poodle. Assemble the Cupcake Bouquet® with cupcake sticks and holders now in place, wrap the boa around bottom of the cupcake sticks and glue in place. Wrap ribbon around each cupcake holder and glue in place. Alternating flowers with dog bones, glue onto each cupcake holder. Using a number 233 hair tube, pipe on the chocolate frosting on each cupcake. Place three dog bone candies, standing up, in the center of each cupcake. Place on cupcake per holder. On the day of the tea party, cover the table with the tablecloth and place the 16 inch board on the center of the table. Centering the 14 inch cake decorating board, place it on top of the 16 inch board. Wrap the boa around the outside of the 16 inch board. Place the Wilton Cupcake Bouquet® in the center of the 14 inch board. Place stuffed French poodle animals around the outside board.

 ## Top Hats for the Boys
Yield: 2 hats

2 black top hats
1-6 foot white boa
2 pom-poms
2-5x5 inch poodle appliqué

Measure the circumference of the bottom rim of the hat. Cut boa (approximately 22 inches per hat) and hot glue in place. Glue a pom-pom on the tail. Glue the poodle appliqué on the front center of the hat over the boa trim for each hat.

 ## Poodle Hats for the Girls
Yield: 2 poodle hats

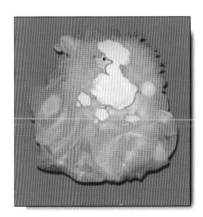

2-15 inch round straw place mats
2-6 inch rounds cut from the middle
   of the straw place mats
3 yards pink organza or toile, divided
pink thread
1-6 foot pink boa, divided
2-6x7 inch poodle appliqués, divided
2 pom-poms
6 flowers with pin backs, divided
hot glue

continued on next page

Draw a 6 inch circle in the center of each place mat. Cut a slit from the bottom of the place mat up to the edge of the marked circle. Cut out the circle. Overlap the cut edges to form the hat the size of the child's head. Fold one yard of material over lengthwise 3 to 4 times to make a 3 inch strip to fit each hat brim. Starting at the back of the hat, place tucks at random in the organza material around the entire hat to cover the red place mat and tack tucks. Set aside. Wrap a strip of boa around the outer edge of the 6 inch cut out for each hat. Glue the poodle appliqué in the center over the boa circle. Glue one pom-pom onto the tail of each poodle appliqué.

Glue the 6 inch poodle appliqué round onto the front of each hat brim. Weave $^1/_2$ yard organza or toile piece (folded 3 to 4 times to make a 3 inch strip) behind the poodle round and glue in place to help round with poodle stand up on the hat. Pin on three flowers on the back of the hat to make it reversible.

Kay Reported the Tea Party for Her Family

At the club meeting, Kay explained that Auntie Starrie covered the table with the tablecloth underlay and overlay. She placed the centerpiece in the middle of the table and set the table with good china. She placed the gift/setting names at each place setting and silver tea service with tea bags, hot water, sugar, sugar cubes and honey at the end of the dining room table. She poured the tea first. She cleared the tea service and then arranged the food on the table. Auntie Starrie also told us we could butler pass the tea party food once the guests were seated.

Kay said, that they dressed up for the tea party with party dresses, pink boas, party shoes and yes a pink poodle hat for my sister and herself and top hats for her brothers. They had fun visiting at the party and eating all of the good tea party foods. They often have tea with their mom and enjoy selecting and trying the flavored herbal decaffeinated teas. They enjoy the honey and sugar cubes in the tea. They did not use lemon, but milk instead. They liked the taste of sweet tea. Kay remembered that lemons can curdle or make the tea too tart.

The food was delicious. The children learned tea party manners. It was a very enjoyable afternoon. Auntie Starrie also enjoyed the tea with our family. Auntie Starrie gave each one of them a poodle souvenir and the place setting name gift to remember the tea party. Kay really enjoyed this special tea party experience.

Miss Lacey and the club enjoyed seeing the pictures. Miss Lacey encouraged Kay to wear her poodle hat to school for the last tea party of the year. Miss Lacey also asked Kay if she could use some of her Auntie Starrie's recipes for the club's poodle party. Kay thought that Auntie Starrie wouldn't mind sharing her recipes with the club. However, she would ask for Auntie Starrie's permission.

On the day of the poodle party for the club, Miss Lacey and the 5th grade class prepared the table for the poodles and the students. The tea party sandwiches and fruit were garnished and ready for the student club members.

The big surprise came when Miss Lacey introduced her seated guest poodles from left to right– Dixie, Pixie and Trixie. Her surprise today was the entertainment. Her little darlings would do a couple of dances for the club members. Usually entertainment comes with or after the food service, but today we will do the entertainment first. Please be seated and enjoy. The fifth graders served the food and tea shortly after the entertainment.

Poodle Table Setup

Poodles Dancing for the World Tea Club

At the end of the tea party, Miss Lacey announced that she was retiring. She wanted to spend more time with the triplet poodles. She promised to come back to visit them and attend some of their club meetings. She thanked all the students for their participation during the school year. She had high hopes that all the club members would not only attend teas, but also help their families host a tea in the near future. Always remember to use good manners, not only at a tea but also in their daily lives. A "please" and "thank you" is definitely sweet music to her ears. So!!!!!!

Bon Voyage and enjoy my new book, "A World of Tea Parties, Just for Kids."

Index